CU00660392

First Marathon Training

A Three Month Training Plan and Journal for Runners

Disclaimer

Custom Programming

This program was specifically developed by a team of experienced marathoners for first time marathon runners.

Workouts
72

Miles
345

Marathon Time
04:30:00 to 5:30:00

Congratulations!

We are excited to be your coaches as you embark on the journey of completing a marathon.

This book was developed to help you achieve your goal of running your first marathon. These numbers have been specifically formatted and are designed to train any runner who follows the plan to finish his or her 26.2 mile adventure between 4.5 and 5.5 hours. If this range falls within your desired time, try to follow the prescribed plan as closely as possible to achieve optimal results.

With that being said, if you miss a workout, do not fret. Life happens! One of the great things that marathon training teaches you is that through all of the peaks and valleys, you are strong enough to persevere and meet your goal. If the assigned days do not work for your specific schedule, please feel free to rearrange them as needed.

This training plan has been organized into a 12 week program. Each page contains one week of the plan.

You will find each day's prescribed workout and then an area for you to record your actual workout. It is important that you record your actual times and any other notes to help your training (how you felt that day, how many hours you slept, weather, caloric intake, etc.)

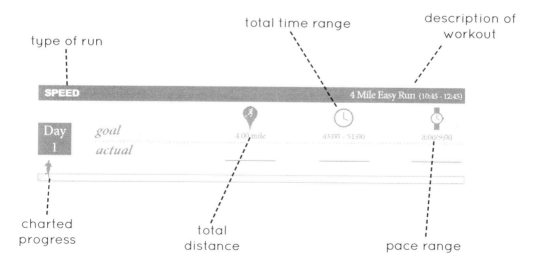

total time range

description of workout

type of run

SPEED   4 Mile Easy Run (10:45 - 12:45)

Day 1   *goal*   *actual*

4.00 mile   43:00 - 51:00   3:00/9:00

charted progress

total distance

pace range

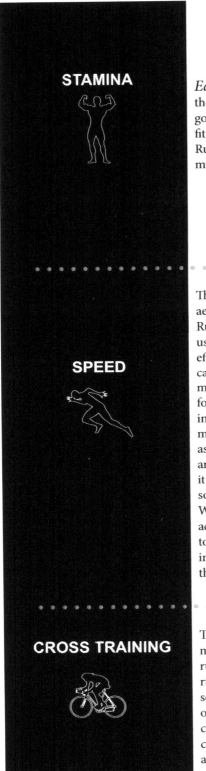

STAMINA

SPEED

CROSS TRAINING

Easy Run: When performing an easy run, be sure to resist the temptation to run faster than the prescribed time. The goal of the Easy Run is to maintain your achieved aerobic fitness gains, not to increase speed and endurance. Easy Runs are less stressful on your body but still allow your muscles to become conditioned.

The purpose of Speed workouts is to hit your maximum aerobic capacity and improve your running economy. Running economy is a measure of how efficiently a person uses oxygen while running at a given pace. The more efficiently you use oxygen, the longer and harder you can run. These workouts can be done at a track or can be measured out using a GPS watch. These sprints are essential for a runner trying to get faster. The workouts prescribed include running quickly at repeated distances of either 0.25 mile (400m), 0.5 mile (800m), or 1 mile (1600m) with an assigned amount of rest between each sprint. Because you are exerting maximum effort or close to maximum effort, it is imperative that you rest for the entire prescribed time so you have enough time to recover between each sprint. When you allow for this full recovery, you will be able to achieve maximum effort for each repeat. Causing lactic acid to enter your body through maximum effort, followed by an immediate resting period causes an adaptation in your body that results in a greater VO_2 max capacity.

The purposes of cross training are to work out different muscle groups, strengthen the muscles that support your running, avoid injury, and provide a mental break from running. This is where you as a runner can be creative. Pick something that you really love and enjoy! Some examples of cross training include yoga, weight lifting, swimming, cycling, hiking, major sports, crossfit, and many more. Each cross training workout should last between 30-60 minutes and does not have to be the same activity every week.

This is a day to listen to your body. If you are completely exhausted, taking a rest day would be more beneficial for your training. If you are feeling great, perform the recovery jog. The purpose of the Recovery jog is to deliver nutrients to your muscles so they can rebuild and repair themselves. This pace will seem very easy at first, but in order to sustain your training for the week and perform the workouts at the prescribed times, you must resist the temptation to run fast.

The purpose of the Steady State run is to teach your body to learn how to transfer oxygen and utilize fuel at a steady and hard pace. Steady State means that your body is using oxygen at the exact same rate that it is burning it. Theoretically, as long as fuel is maintained, you should be able to hold this pace for miles on end.

The purpose of the Long Run is to mentally prepare you for the distance of the marathon and to get your body used to delivering oxygen and nutrients for an extended period of time. The Long Run is a great opportunity for you to test out your fueling strategies for the actual marathon. Do your best to finish the Long Run without stopping. Stay at the pace assigned (even if you feel that you can go faster) because the pace assigned will allow you to finish the entire run.

The purpose of this day is to allow your hard worked muscles to replenish themselves. Eat well, drink water, and REST. Your body needs it.

RECOVERY

STEADY-STATE

LONG RUN

REST

In addition to the runs and workouts that we have provided for you, the following components need to be included in your comprehensive training program:

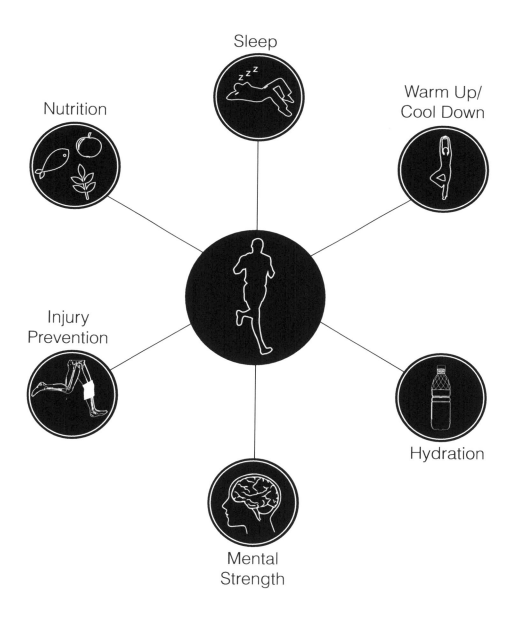

Sleep

Warm Up/ Cool Down

Nutrition

Injury Prevention

Hydration

Mental Strength

Sleep

Sufficient sleep is one of the most important components of your success. Sleep is commonly forgotten as a key component to training, but many injuries and overtraining can be a result of lack of sleep. The goal is to sleep for at least eight hours every night. When you are asleep, your body is actively working to rebuild the muscle cells that you have broken down with your running and cross training. A few ways to ensure that you receive adequate sleep is to maintain a regular sleep schedule, establish a bedtime routine, avoid caffeine and alcohol close to bedtime, avoid heavy exercise close to bed time, create an electronic and light free sleeping area, and avoid large meals before bedtime.

Warm Up/
Cool Down

Why is warming up so important? The purpose of warming up is to literally raise the temperature of your muscles, raise your heart rate, and dilate your blood vessels. All of these are important because they help to minimize stress to your heart when you begin running, supply your muscles with oxygen, and give your muscles flexibility. The warm-up is not intended to exhaust you. Investing a simple 5-10 minutes to your warm-up is all that is necessary.

Warm Up:
1. Foam Roll
2. Slow aerobic exercise (walk, jog, row, cycle, jump rope) - 2-3 minutes
3. Increase tempo - 2-3 minutes
4. Dynamic exercise (high knees, butt kickers, grapevine, skips)

Cool Down
1. Slow down and jog - 1-2 minutes
2. Walk at fast pace - 1-5 minutes
3. Stretch and foam roll

Hydration

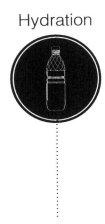

A good rule of thumb regarding hydration is to drink half of your body weight in oz. For example, if a woman weighs 140 pounds, then she should drink 70 oz. of water per day. As a runner, you should aim to drink 1.5x to 2x that number, especially if you are training in a humid climate or at a high altitude. Take water with you on any run that is over 5 miles. During the marathon, drink water at every stop.

Mental Strength

Throughout your journey, keep in mind that running a marathon is parallel with life. You will go through ups and downs, triumphs and defeats, but in the end you will accomplish your goal. You will look back and be proud of the adversity that you faced and persevered through. From past experiences, we have three tips/tricks that you can use during your training.

1. *Visualizing*

   Lay in a dim room and close your eyes. Visualize yourself crossing the finish line. Imagine how happy you are, how strong you feel, and how great your body feels. It has been proven that athletes who visualize success are more prone to achieving success.

2. *Writing affirmations*

   At any point during your training you can start writing lists of affirmations to yourself. The purpose of this is to place yourself in a positive mindset. This is especially important to do the night before a race. Some examples of affirmations include
   - I will finish this race.
   - My training has completely prepared me for this race.
   - My legs are strong and will carry me the 26.2 miles.
   - I have mentally prepared and am unstoppable.
   - I will finish this marathon without walking.

3. *Making Goals*

   Every goal that you make should be realistic, measurable, and attainable but also challenging. Set short term and long term goals. Set a goal every week during your training. For example: Week 1 goal may be…. "I will finish each run without walking and will only drink wine twice this week." Your long term goal may be… "I will finish my marathon in under six hours." Make sure that you revisit your goals at least once a week. Post your goals somewhere where you will see them often, such as your bathroom mirror, your fridge, or the background of your computer screen.

4. *Motivational Phrase*

Have a key word or phrase that will help you persevere when you start to feel uncomfortable or fatigued. A few recommended words are "I am strong", "I have trained hard enough for this", "I can finish", "strength", etc.

5. *Frame of Mind*

While you are running, find the frame of mind that fits you best:

    a. Take the opportunity to let your mind be free and travel whichever way it desires. You will notice that you may end up coming up with some of your best ideas.

    b. Jam out to your favorite type of music. You can find playlists online that have songs with a beat that matches your specific pace.

    c. Pray or meditate.

Injury Prevention

Injury	What is it?	Symptoms	Causes	Workouts	Rehab
Achilles Tendinitis	Tightness/ irritation of tendon between calf muscles & back of heel.	Pain & swelling above heel. Pain when standing on toes.	Extreme increase in training. Tight and/or weak calves.	Take a few days off. Elliptical or pool.	Ice. Strengthen calves. Foam roll calves.
Runners Knee	Irritation of cartilage inside of kneecap.	Pain inside knee. Pain in knee after sitting for long periods of time. Pain while walking down stairs.	Overpronation. Weak quads, hips, glutes.	Take extra rest days & reduce mileage. Lower impact training (elliptical, biking, swimming). Uphill running (you can simulate on treadmill).	Strengthen hip and glute muscles. Stretch hip flexors. Ice. Foam roll: glutes, hamstrings, quads, calves.
Plantar Fasciitis	Small tears & inflammation in tendons & ligaments that run from heel to toe.	Dull ache along arch or bottom of heel. Pain is worse in morning.	Very high/very low arches. Pronation. Supination. Increasing mileage too quickly. Tight hip flexors. Weak core muscles.	Pool run. Swim. Biking. Elliptical. Extra rest days.	Ice. Stretch plantar fascia. Stretch calves. Get proper shoes. Foam roll: calves. Lacrosse ball: bottom of foot.
IT Band Syndrome	The iliotibial band, the ligament that runs down the outside of the thigh from hip to shin is tight or inflamed.	Swelling and pain on outside of knee.	Wearing worn out shoes. Running too many miles. Over pronation. Weak gluteal muscles.	Pool run. Swim. Biking. Elliptical. Extra rest days.	Foam roll: IT Band, quads, hamstrings, glutes.
Shin Splints	Micro fractures in shin. Micro tears in posterior and anterior shin muscles.	Shin pain.	Tight calf muscles. Weak shin muscles. Pronation or supination Flat feet. Overtraining.	Reduce mileage for a few days and take extra rest days. Pool run. Swim.	Ice. Foam roll: calves. *If the pain does not get better in a few days, consult doctor. You may have a stress fracture.

Nutrition

Power Foods For Runners:

Sweet Potatoes
Cottage Cheese
Bananas
Almond Butter
Quinoa
Coffee
Eggs
Kale
Avocado
Salmon
Berries
Lean Beef

Daily Meals

Breakfast
Mid Morning Snack
Lunch
Mid Afternoon Snack
Dinner

Foods to Avoid

Processed Foods
Alcohol (in excess)
Processed Sugar
Fried Foods
Soda

In summary, aim for a well-balanced diet that focuses on high-quality ingredients, but more importantly, avoid processed foods. Listen to your body and learn what types of foods have a positive or negative impact on your performance and make the proper adjustments. Sufficient caloric intake is imperative to promote recovery, combat fatigue, and rebuild your muscles.

Common Marathon Mistakes and How to Avoid Them

Starting Out Too Fast

This is the most common mistake among marathon rookies. Once you arrive at the start line, you will immediately sense the energy in the air. Surrounding yourself with a large group of lunatics who are actually excited to wake up hours before the sunrise and *pay money* to run 26.2 miles, unavoidably gets the adrenaline pumping. This rush of adrenaline is what causes people to start too fast. The best way to avoid this is to simply be conscious of it. Check your watch to ensure that you stay within your goal pace. Most advanced marathoners will tell you that their goal is to have a negative split. This means that they run the second half of the marathon (13.1 miles) faster than the first.

Changing Your Diet The Week of the Marathon

As race day approaches, diet and nutrition inevitably moves to the forefront of your concerns. You will be exposed to a variety of conflicting philosophies on foods to eat and foods to avoid. If you are going to experiment with food, do it while you are training. It is imperative that you do not change your diet or introduce any new foods the week leading up to the race or the day of your marathon. Trying new foods and changing your dietary habits puts you at risk for your body rejecting the food. If you plan on using a gel or salt tablet during your race, be sure to test them out during your long runs. We recommend that you take a gel every 7 miles and a salt tablet at mile 10 and mile 20. If your body rejects a new food on race day, you could be facing an array of GI issues (diarrhea, constipation, vomiting, upset stomach). Stick to your diet - don't be tempted by the newest and greatest "magic quinoa and kale speed and energy booster".

Not Drinking Water at Every Stop

Drink stations are usually dispersed at 1 or 2 mile intervals for the duration of the race. It is critical that you take at least one sip at every station, even if you do not feel thirsty. People tend to not feel as thirsty in a cooler climate and in the beginning of the race. Being thirsty is a sign of dehydration, so be proactive and stay hydrated.

Not Breaking in Your Running Gear

If your parents buy you a brand new pair of running shoes two days before your big race, promptly thank them, then put the shoes back in the box until you begin training for your next marathon. Trying out new running gear the week of your race can lead to problems such as chafing, blistering, and possible injuries. You may have heard jokes about runners not having any toenails. If you would like to stay out of the "no toenail club" make sure to break in your properly fitted shoes at least 3 weeks before your race. It will also help if you keep your toenails trimmed and your feet dry by wearing moisture-wicking socks. Using broken-in shoes will also reduce your risk of developing a blister during the race.

Chafing

Since running is a repetitive movement, your clothes will be in a friction battle with your skin for 26.2 miles. To avoid painful chafing, we recommend rubbing a lubricant anywhere that you anticipate friction. Some common areas include inner thighs, armpits, and nipples.

Arriving Late

You will be dealing with a large crowd of people who are all trying to properly prepare for the race. This means there will be lines everywhere - at the bathrooms, the gear drop-off station, and the start line. The pedestrian traffic will be nothing compared to the vehicular traffic, as everyone will be scrambling to find a last minute parking spot. Be sure to get to the marathon early so you can have everything checked in, get your final bathroom break, and properly warm up. A good rule of thumb is to plan your arrival for at least 1 hour prior to start time.

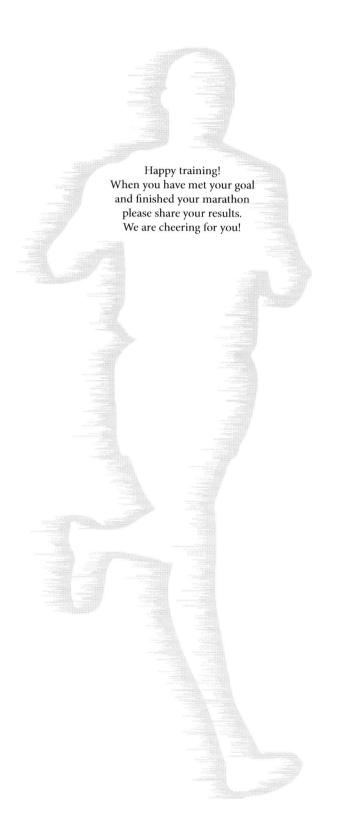

Happy training!
When you have met your goal
and finished your marathon
please share your results.
We are cheering for you!

EASY   4 Mile Easy Run (10:45 - 12:45)

Day 1

goal   4.00 mile   43:00 - 51:00   10:45 - 12:45

actual

SPEED   1 Mile Repeats (2 miles at 8:50 - 10:40 pace) 5 min rest in between

Day 2

goal   2.00 mile   22:40 - 26:20   8:50 - 10:40

actual

CROSS TRAIN

Day 3

goal

actual

RECOVERY   Rest *or* 3 Mile Recovery Run (11:50 - 13:30 pace)

Day 4

goal   3.00 mile   35:30 - 40:30   11:50 - 13:30

actual

STEADY   5 Miles (9:45 - 11:40 pace)

Day 5

goal   5.00 mile   48:30 - 58:20   9:45 - 11:40

actual

LONG   8 Mile Long Run (11:15 - 13:05 pace)

Day 6

goal   8.00 mile   01:30:00-1:44:40   11:15 - 13:05

actual

REST

Day 7

STAMINA
5 Mile Easy Run (10:45 - 12:40 pace)

Day 8

goal — 5.00 mile — 53:45-01:03:20 — 10:45 - 12:40

actual — _____ — _____ — _____

SPEED
4 x 800m (4:05 min - 5:00 min pace) 2 min rest in between

Day 9

goal — 2.00 mile — 22:20 - 26:00 — 4:05 - 5:00

actual — _____ — _____ — _____

CROSS TRAIN

Day 10

goal

actual

RECOVERY
Rest or 2 Mile Recovery Run (11:30 - 13:15 pace)

Day 11

goal — 2.00 mile — 23:00 - 26:30 — 11:30 - 13:15

actual — _____ — _____ — _____

STEADY
5 Miles (9:35 - 11:50 pace)

Day 12

goal — 5.00 mile — 47:55 - 59:10 — 9:35 - 11:50

actual — _____ — _____ — _____

LONG
10 Mile Long Run (11:05 - 13:15 pace)

Day 13

goal — 10.00 mile — 01:50:50 - 02:12:30 — 11:05 - 13:15

actual — _____ — _____ — _____

REST

Day 14

STAMINA — 4 Mile Easy Run (10:30 - 12:15 pace)

Day 15
goal — 4.00 mile — 42:00 - 49:00 — 10:30 - 12:15
actual

SPEED — 6 x 400m (1:58 min - 2:24 min pace) 3 min rest in between

Day 16
goal — 1.50 mile — 26:48 - 29:24 — 1:58 - 2:24
actual

CROSS TRAIN

Day 17
goal
actual

RECOVERY — Rest or 3 Mile Recovery Run (11:30 - 13:40 pace)

Day 18
goal — 3.00 mile — 34:30 - 41:00 — 11:30 -13:40
actual

STEADY — 6 Miles (9:25 - 11:50 pace)

Day 19
goal — 6.00 mile — 56:30 - 01:11:00 — 9:25 -11:50
actual

LONG — 12 Mile Long Run (10:40 -13:00 pace)

Day 20
goal — 12.00 mile — 02:08:00 - 02:36:00 — 10:40 - 13:00
actual

REST

Day 21

STAMINA

4 Mile Easy Run (10:20 - 12:20 pace)

Day 22

goal — 4.00 mile — 41:20 - 49:20 — 10:20 - 12:20

actual

SPEED

1 Mile Repeats (3 miles at 8:35 - 10:35 pace) 3 min rest in between

Day 23

goal — 3.00 mile — 31:45 - 37:45 — 8:35 - 10:35

actual

CROSS TRAIN

Day 24

goal

actual

RECOVERY

Rest *or* 2 Mile Recovery Run (11:25 - 13:30 pace)

Day 25

goal — 2.00 mile — 22:50 - 27:00 — 11:25 - 13:30

actual

STEADY

6 Miles (9:35 - 11:20 pace)

Day 26

goal — 6.00 mile — 57:30 - 01:08:00 — 9:35 - 11:20

actual

LONG

14 Mile Long Run (10:25 - 13:10 pace)

Day 27

goal — 14.00 mile — 2:25:50-03:04:20 — 10:25 - 13:10

actual

REST

Day 28

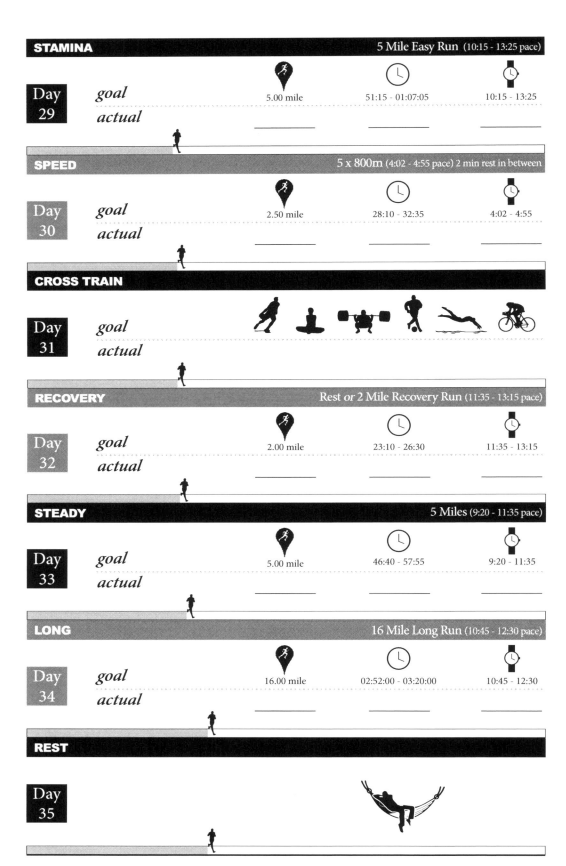

STAMINA — 5 Mile Easy Run (10:15 - 13:25 pace)

Day 29

goal	5.00 mile	51:15 - 01:07:05	10:15 - 13:25
actual			

SPEED — 5 x 800m (4:02 - 4:55 pace) 2 min rest in between

Day 30

goal	2.50 mile	28:10 - 32:35	4:02 - 4:55
actual			

CROSS TRAIN

Day 31

goal	
actual	

RECOVERY — Rest or 2 Mile Recovery Run (11:35 - 13:15 pace)

Day 32

goal	2.00 mile	23:10 - 26:30	11:35 - 13:15
actual			

STEADY — 5 Miles (9:20 - 11:35 pace)

Day 33

goal	5.00 mile	46:40 - 57:55	9:20 - 11:35
actual			

LONG — 16 Mile Long Run (10:45 - 12:30 pace)

Day 34

goal	16.00 mile	02:52:00 - 03:20:00	10:45 - 12:30
actual			

REST

Day 35

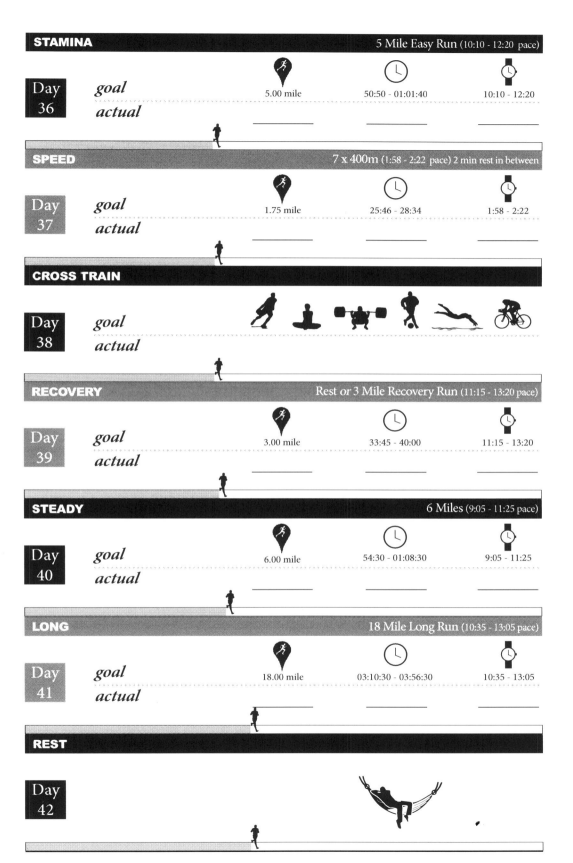

STAMINA — 5 Mile Easy Run (10:10 - 12:20 pace)

Day 36

	distance	time	pace
goal	5.00 mile	50:50 - 01:01:40	10:10 - 12:20
actual			

SPEED — 7 x 400m (1:58 - 2:22 pace) 2 min rest in between

Day 37

	distance	time	pace
goal	1.75 mile	25:46 - 28:34	1:58 - 2:22
actual			

CROSS TRAIN

Day 38

goal			
actual			

RECOVERY — Rest *or* 3 Mile Recovery Run (11:15 - 13:20 pace)

Day 39

	distance	time	pace
goal	3.00 mile	33:45 - 40:00	11:15 - 13:20
actual			

STEADY — 6 Miles (9:05 - 11:25 pace)

Day 40

	distance	time	pace
goal	6.00 mile	54:30 - 01:08:30	9:05 - 11:25
actual			

LONG — 18 Mile Long Run (10:35 - 13:05 pace)

Day 41

	distance	time	pace
goal	18.00 mile	03:10:30 - 03:56:30	10:35 - 13:05
actual			

REST

Day 42

STAMINA 5 Mile Easy Run (10:15 - 12:40 pace)

Day 43
goal   5.00 mile   51:15 - 01:03:20   10:15 - 12:40
actual

SPEED 6 x 800m (4:07 - 5:00 pace) 2 min rest in between

Day 44
goal   3.00 mile   34:42 - 40:00   4:07 - 5:00
actual

CROSS TRAIN

Day 45
goal
actual

RECOVERY Rest or 3 Mile Recovery Run (11:35 - 13:50 pace)

Day 46
goal   3.00 mile   34:45 - 41:30   11:35 - 13:50
actual

STEADY 5 Miles (8:55 - 11:15 pace)

Day 47
goal   5.00 mile   44:35 - 56:15   8:55 - 11:15
actual

LONG 20 Mile Long Run (10:35 - 13:05 pace)

Day 48
goal   20.00 mile   03:31:40 - 04:21:40   10:35 - 13:05
actual

REST

Day 49

STAMINA   6 Mile Easy Run (9:30 - 12:25 pace)

Day 50   *goal*   6.00 mile   57:00 - 01:14:30   9:30 - 12:25
             actual   _____   _____   _____

SPEED   1 Mile Repeats (4 miles at 8:40 - 10:45 pace 3 min rest in between)

Day 51   *goal*   4.00 mile   43:40 - 52:00   8:40 - 10:45
             actual   _____   _____   _____

CROSS TRAIN

Day 52   *goal*
             actual

RECOVERY   Rest or 3 Mile Recovery Run (11:20-13:55 pace)

Day 53   *goal*   3.00 mile   34:00 - 41:45   11:20 - 13:55
             actual   _____   _____   _____

STEADY   5 Miles (10:25-11:40 pace)

Day 54   *goal*   5.00 mile   52:05 - 58:20   10:25 -11:40
             actual   _____   _____   _____

LONG   22 Mile Long Run (10:50-13:10 pace)

Day 55   *goal*   22.00 mile   03:58:20 - 4:49:40   10:50 - 13:10
             actual   _____   _____   _____

REST

Day 56

STAMINA — 5 Mile Easy Run (10:50-12:50)

Day 57

	mile	time	pace
goal	5.00 mile	54:10 - 01:04:10	10:50 - 12:50
actual			

SPEED — 8 x 800m (4:00-4:50 pace) 3 min rest in between

Day 58

	mile	time	pace
goal	4.00 mile	53:00 - 59:40	4:00 - 4:50
actual			

CROSS TRAIN

Day 59

goal	
actual	

RECOVERY — Rest or 2 Mile Recovery Run (11:35 - 13:10 pace)

Day 60

	mile	time	pace
goal	2.00 mile	23:10 - 26:20	11:35 - 13:10
actual			

STEADY — 6 Miles (9:10-11:20 pace)

Day 61

	mile	time	pace
goal	6.00 mile	55:00 - 01:08:00	9:10 - 11:20
actual			

LONG — 15 Mile Long Run (10:45 - 13:05 pace)

Day 62

	mile	time	pace
goal	15.00 mile	2:41:15-03:16:15	10:45 - 13:05
actual			

REST

Day 63

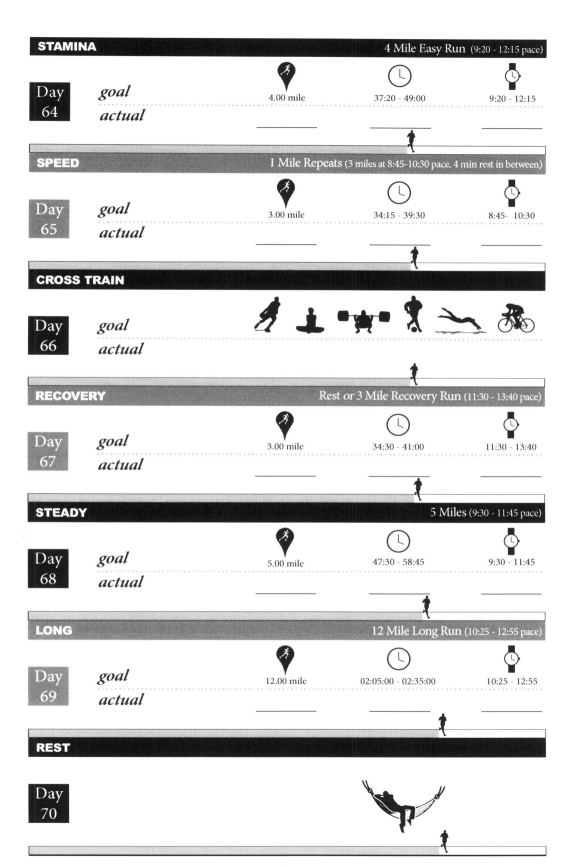

STAMINA 4 Mile Easy Run (9:20 - 12:15 pace)

Day 64

goal — 4.00 mile | 37:20 - 49:00 | 9:20 - 12:15

actual

SPEED 1 Mile Repeats (3 miles at 8:45-10:30 pace, 4 min rest in between)

Day 65

goal — 3.00 mile | 34:15 - 39:30 | 8:45 - 10:30

actual

CROSS TRAIN

Day 66

goal

actual

RECOVERY Rest or 3 Mile Recovery Run (11:30 - 13:40 pace)

Day 67

goal — 3.00 mile | 34:30 - 41:00 | 11:30 - 13:40

actual

STEADY 5 Miles (9:30 - 11:45 pace)

Day 68

goal — 5.00 mile | 47:30 - 58:45 | 9:30 - 11:45

actual

LONG 12 Mile Long Run (10:25 - 12:55 pace)

Day 69

goal — 12.00 mile | 02:05:00 - 02:35:00 | 10:25 - 12:55

actual

REST

Day 70

35

STAMINA   5 Mile Easy Run (10:10 - 12:35 pace)

Day 71

goal   5.00 mile   55:50 - 01:02:55   10:10 - 12:35

actual

SPEED   4 x 800m (4:05 - 4:55 pace) 3 min rest in between

Day 72

goal   2.00 mile   25:20 - 28:40   4:05 - 4:55

actual

CROSS TRAIN

Day 73

goal

actual

RECOVERY   Rest *or* 2 Mile Recovery Run (11:15 - 13:35 pace)

Day 74

goal   2.00 mile   22:30 - 27:10   11:15 - 13:35

actual

STEADY   5 Miles (9:10 - 11:10 pace)

Day 75

goal   5.00 mile   45:50 - 55:50   9:10 -11:10

actual

LONG   8 Mile Long Run (10:00 - 12:25 pace)

Day 76

goal   8.00 mile   01:20:00 - 01:39:20   10:00 - 12:25

actual

REST

Day 77

STAMINA — 6 Mile Easy Run (10:35 - 12:20 pace)

Day 78

goal — 6.00 mile — 01:03:20 - 01:14:00 — 10:35 - 12:20

actual

CROSS TRAIN

Day 79

goal

actual

STAMINA — 4 Mile Easy Run (10:45 - 12:15 pace)

Day 80

goal — 4.00 mile — 43:00 - 49:00 — 10:45 - 12:15

actual

REST

Day 81

PRE-RACE — 2 Mile Slow Jog (10:55 - 12:50 pace)

Day 82

goal — 2.00 mile — 21:50 - 25:40 — 10:55 - 12:50

actual

RACE DAY

Day 83

see next page for split times

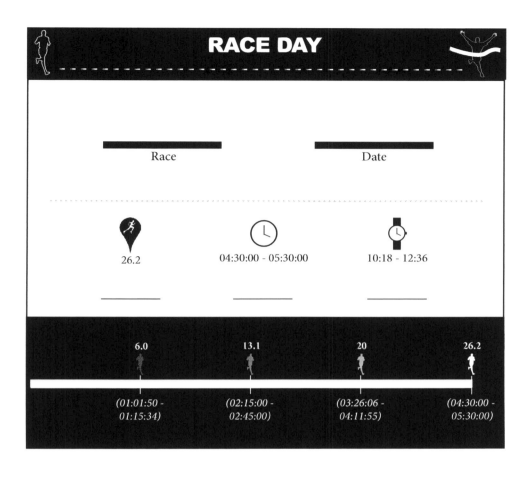

Race   Date

26.2   04:30:00 - 05:30:00   10:18 - 12:36

6.0	13.1	20	26.2
(01:01:50 - 01:15:34)	(02:15:00 - 02:45:00)	(03:26:06 - 04:11:55)	(04:30:00 - 05:30:00)

notes

Congratulations on your tremendous accomplishment! You are now part of an elite group. Thank you for trusting us with your marathon training by utilizing this marathon plan as your training and accountability partner. We hope that you have become as hooked to marathon running as we are and decide to sign up for another race. As you continue to improve as a runner, you may want to challenge yourself to cross the finish line even faster. To help you track your continuous improvement, we have developed a number of customized training plans depending on your specific time goal.

The two that you may be interested in after completing this training plan are:
- *Sub 5 Hour Marathon*
- *Sub 4 Hour Marathon*

Printed in Great Britain
by Amazon

32235495R00024